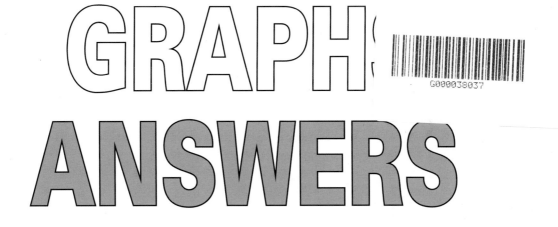

GRAPHS
ANSWERS

COMPLETE ANSWERS TO QUESTIONS IN
'EVERYDAY GRAPHS'
AND
'COORDINATE GRAPHS'

PETER ROBSON

 **Newby Books**

PO Box 40, Scarborough
North Yorkshire, YO12 5TW
Telephone/Fax 01723 362713
www.newbybooks.co.uk

First published 1993
Fourth Impression 2008
© Peter Robson 1993
ISBN 978-1-872686-16-5

Printed by G. H. Smith & Son, Easingwold, York YO61 3AB
Telephone 01347 821329. Facsimile 01347 822576
www.ghsmith.com

1.(a) Monday 30, Tuesday 40,
Wednesday 15, Thursday 25,
Friday 50, Saturday 45.

   (b) 205

2.(Suggestion)

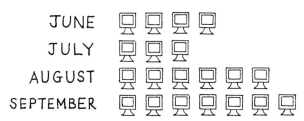

JUNE

JULY

AUGUST

SEPTEMBER

Pictogram to show sales of
television sets at a shop
(⊟ represents 5 TV sets)

3.(Suggestion)

Carl   ◗◗◗

Liz   ◗◗◗◗◗◗◗

Sophie   ◗◗◗◗

William   ◗◗◗◗◗◗◗◗

Pictogram to show numbers of balloons
at people's parties (◗ represents 10 balloons)

4.Chimpanzee's Weekly about 22500
Amateur Grumbling 15000
Slug and Snail about 27500
Toes Illustrated 25000

5.(Suggestion)

Adderbrook

Delville

Eston

Hillhead

Westwick

PICTOGRAM TO SHOW NUMBERS OF TREES
IN FIVE DIFFERENT FORESTS
(🌲 REPRESENTS 1 MILLION TREES)

6.(Suggestion)

Barnborough

Dunnerby

Firlington

Rywood

Sedgeworth

Pictogram to show numbers of
buses kept at 5 depots
(🚌 represents 10 buses)

7.(Suggestion)

0900 -1000

1000 -1100

1100 -1200

1200 -1300

1300 -1400

1400 -1500

1500 -1600

1600 -1700

1700 -1800

Pictogram showing sales of ice-cream cones
for each hour of a day (represents 10 cones)

8.(a)January (b)October (c) April
and September (d)85mm (e)910mm
(f)75.833rec or 75⅚ mm (g)July

9.(a)(Suggestion)

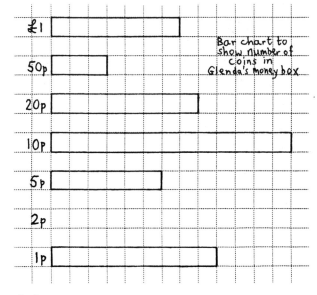

Bar chart to
show number of
coins in
Glenda's money box

£1

50p

20p

10p

5p

2p

1p

(b) £11.79

10.(Suggestion)

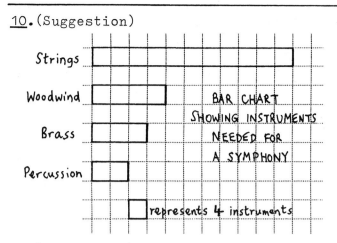

11.(Suggestion)

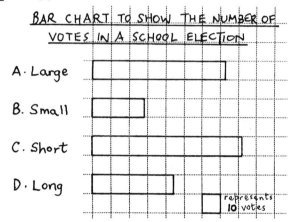

12. (a)20000ha (b)30000ha
(c)Clwyd 240000; Dyfed 580000;
Gwent 140000; Gwynedd 390000;
Mid Glamorgan 100000; Powys 510000;
South Glamorgan 40000;
West Glamorgan 80000.

13.(a)24th; (b) 9; (c)1st, 8th, 21st,
22nd; (d)155; (e)Average daily hours
of sunshine ($^{155}/_{31}$ = 5). Same number
shaded above line as unshaded below
line; (f)4.4999rec hours.

14.(Suggestion)

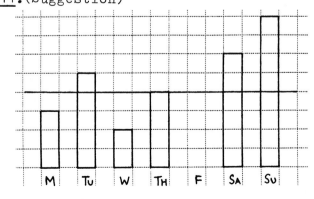

Column graph to show number
of toffees eaten by Terry

(Average is 4 toffees)

15.(a)4
   (b)(i)84 (ii)140 (iii)176
   (c)(i)32 (ii)92 (iii)116
   (d)(i)28 (ii)44 (iii)76

16.

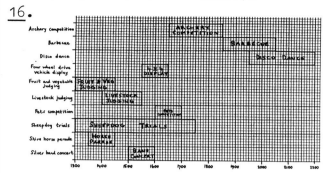

17.(a),(b)

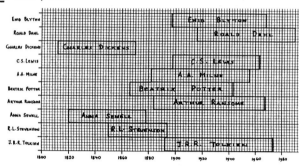

(c)Black Beauty-Anna Sewell
Charlie and the C.F.-Roald Dahl
Coot Club-Arthur Ransome
Five on a Secret Trail-Enid Blyton
The Hobbit-J.R.R.Tolkien
The Horse and His Boy-C.S.Lewis
Oliver Twist-Charles Dickens
Tale of Peter Rabbit-Beatrix Potter
Treasure Island-R.L.Stevenson
Winnie-the-Pooh- A.A.Milne

18.(a)14 (b)17 (c)26 (d)10 (e)22

19.

Tally	Frequency
⊞⊞ ⊞⊞ III	13
⊞⊞ ⊞⊞ ⊞⊞ ⊞⊞	20
⊞⊞ ⊞⊞ ⊞⊞ ⊞⊞ ⊞⊞ ⊞⊞ ⊞⊞ IIII	39
⊞⊞ ⊞⊞ ⊞⊞ ⊞⊞ ⊞⊞ II	27
⊞⊞ ⊞⊞ ⊞⊞ ⊞⊞ ⊞⊞ ⊞⊞ III	33

20.

Ticket colour	Tally	Total (Frequency)
YELLOW	⊞⊞ ⊞⊞ ⊞⊞ ⊞⊞ I	21
BLUE	⊞⊞ II	7
RED	⊞⊞ ⊞⊞ ⊞⊞ I	16
GREEN	⊞⊞ I	6

21.

Number of letters in word	1	2	3	4	5	6	7	8	9	10
Frequency	2	4	8	7	5	3	1	1	0	2

22.

Height	Shorter than 101 cm	101 to 120 cm	121 to 140 cm	141 to 160 cm	Taller than 160 cm
Number of People	1	3	5	7	4

23.(a)

SCORE	2	3	4	5	6	7	8	9	10	11	12
FREQUENCY	6	5	5	8	10	18	17	13	7	6	5

(b) The <u>calculated</u> likelihood of each score, to the nearest whole number, is

SCORE	2	3	4	5	6	7	8	9	10	11	12
FREQUENCY	3	6	8	11	14	17	14	11	8	6	3

(Yes.This does add up to 101 !)

(c) 7

24.(a)

Age	7	8	9	10	11	12
Number of children (Frequency)	6	10	14	8	9	3

(b)(Suggestion)

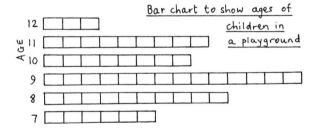

Bar chart to show ages of children in a playground

(c)

Age	7 and 8	9 and 10	11 and 12
Frequency	16	22	12

(d)(Suggestion)

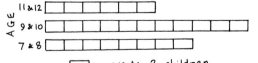

represents 2 children

25.(a) 5

(b)
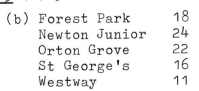

Forest Park   18
Newton Junior   24
Orton Grove   22
St George's   16
Westway   11

(c)(Suggestion)

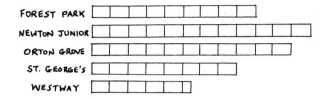

FOREST PARK
NEWTON JUNIOR
ORTON GROVE
ST. GEORGE'S
WESTWAY

represents 2 goals

(d)(i) 10   (ii) 6   (iii) 4

(e)(Suggestion)

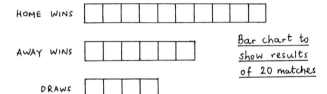

HOME WINS

AWAY WINS

DRAWS

Bar chart to show results of 20 matches

(f) Newton Junior

(g) 0 goals...1   6 goals...2
    1 goal....1   7 goals...1
    2 goals...1   8 goals...1
    3 goals...3   9 goals...0
    4 goals...3   10 goals...1
    5 goals...6

(h)

Number of goals in a match	0	1	2	3	4	5	6	7	8	9	10
Number of matches with this number of goals	1	1	1	3	3	6	2	1	1	0	1

(i)

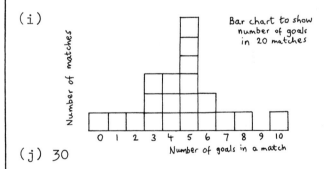

Bar chart to show number of goals in 20 matches

(j) 30

26.(a)

Salary	£0 to £4999	£5000 to £9999	£10000 to £14999	£15000 to £19999	£20000 to £24999	£25000 to £29999	£30000 to £34999
Number of people	1	2	6	4	1	3	1

(b)

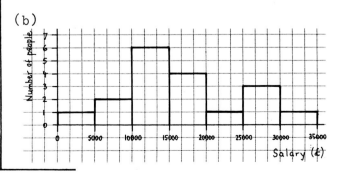

27.(a)

DEPARTURE TIMES	1300 to 1359	1400 to 1459	1500 to 1559	1600 to 1659
FREQUENCY	8	6	5	11

(b)

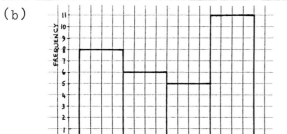

28.(a)

Mass	0 to 19.9 kg	20.0 to 39.9 kg	40.0 to 59.9 kg	60.0 to 79.9 kg	80.0 to 99.9 kg
Frequency	2	5	7	6	3

(b)

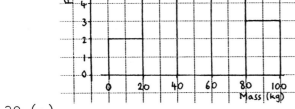

29.(a)

	A	B	C	D	E	F
Mass of parcel	0 to 1.9 kg	2.0 to 3.9 kg	4.0 to 5.9 kg	6.0 to 7.9 kg	8.0 to 9.9 kg	10.0 to 11.9 kg
Number of parcels	1	3	5	6	2	3

(b)

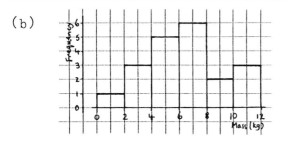

(c) £94

30.(a)

Percentage mark	0 to 19	20 to 39	40 to 59	60 to 79	80 to 99
Frequency	2	6	13	12	7

(b)

31.(a)

Miles	0.5 to 5.5	5.6 to 10.5	10.6 to 15.5	15.6 to 20.5	20.6 to 25.5	25.6 to 30.5	30.6 to 35.5
Frequency	3	4	6	10	7	9	11

(b)

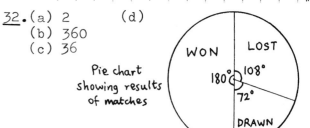

32.(a) 2
(b) 360
(c) 36
(d)

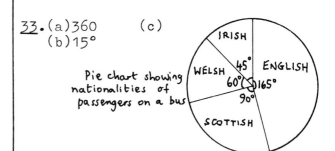

Pie chart showing results of matches

33.(a) 360
(b) 15°
(c)

Pie chart showing nationalities of passengers on a bus

34.(a) 15
(b) 24°
(c)

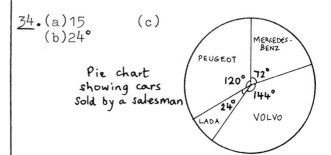

Pie chart showing cars sold by a salesman

35.(Each tourist 20°)

Pie chart showing nationalities of tourists at the Beach Plaza Hotel

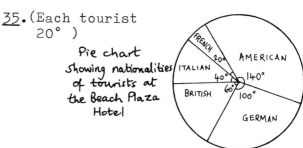

36.(Each child 12°)

Pie chart showing sports activities of a group of children

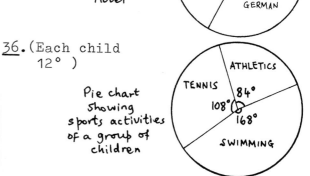

6

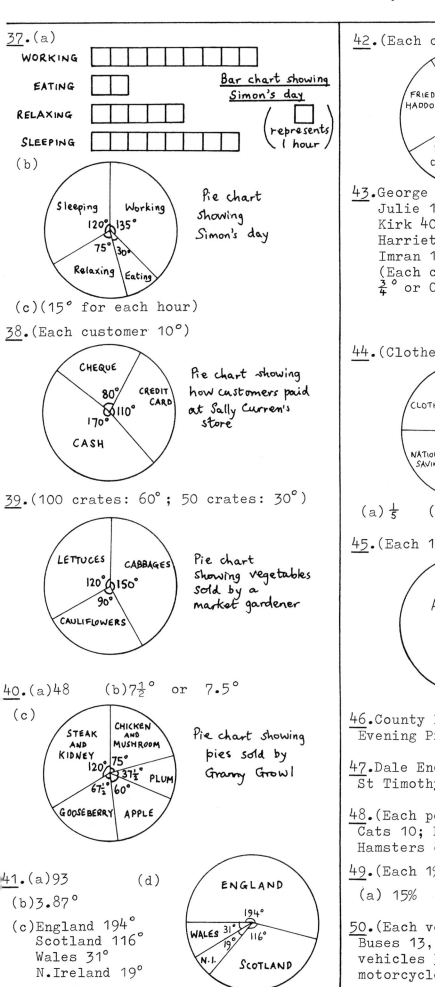

37.(a)

WORKING

EATING

RELAXING

SLEEPING

Bar chart showing
Simon's day

☐ (represents
1 hour)

(b)

Pie chart
showing
Simon's day

Sleeping 120°   Working 135°

75°   30°

Relaxing   Eating

(c)(15° for each hour)

38.(Each customer 10°)

CHEQUE   80°

CREDIT CARD   110°

170°

CASH

Pie chart showing
how customers paid
at Sally Curren's
store

39.(100 crates: 60°; 50 crates: 30°)

LETTUCES   120°   CABBAGES   150°

90°

CAULIFLOWERS

Pie chart
showing vegetables
sold by a
market gardener

40.(a)48   (b)7½° or 7.5°

(c)

STEAK AND KIDNEY   120°   CHICKEN AND MUSHROOM   75°

37½°   PLUM

67½°   60°

GOOSEBERRY   APPLE

Pie chart showing
pies sold by
Granny Growl

41.(a)93   (d)

(b)3.87°

(c)England 194°
Scotland 116°
Wales 31°
N.Ireland 19°

ENGLAND   194°

WALES   31°   116°

19°

N.I.   SCOTLAND

42.(Each customer 3°)

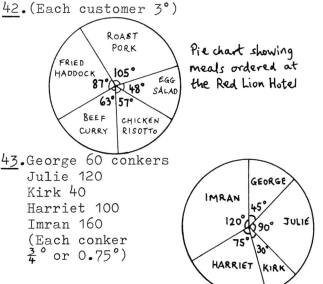

ROAST PORK

FRIED HADDOCK   105°

87°   48°   EGG SALAD

63°   57°

BEEF CURRY   CHICKEN RISOTTO

Pie chart showing
meals ordered at
the Red Lion Hotel

43.George 60 conkers
Julie 120
Kirk 40
Harriet 100
Imran 160
(Each conker
¾° or 0.75°)

GEORGE

IMRAN   45°

120°   90°   JULIE

75°   30°

HARRIET   KIRK

44.(Clothes ⅕ × 360° = 72°, etc.)

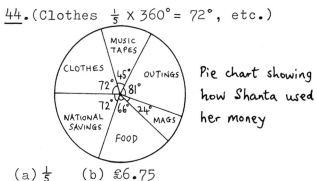

MUSIC TAPES

CLOTHES   45°   OUTINGS

72°   81°

72°   66°   24°   MAGS

NATIONAL SAVINGS

FOOD

Pie chart showing
how Shanta used
her money

(a) ⅕   (b) £6.75

45.(Each 1% needs 3.6°)

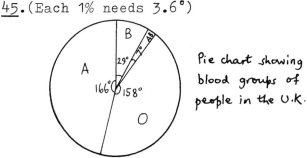

B

A   29°   7°   4°

166°   158°

O

Pie chart showing
blood groups of
people in the U.K.

46.County News 8, Evening Post 15,
Evening Press 11, Herald 6

47.Dale End 31, Killerby Grange 23,
St Timothy's 18

48.(Each pet 8°) Budgerigars 3;
Cats 10; Dogs 12; Goldfish 4;
Hamsters 8; Rabbits 7; Snakes 1.

49.(Each 1% needs 3.6°)

(a) 15%   (b) 25%   (c) 60%

50.(Each vehicle 2½° or 2.5°)
Buses 13, cars 76, heavy goods
vehicles 33, light vans 18,
motorcycles 4.

51. (Each person 20°)
Cocoa 3, coffee 5, orange squash 4,
tea 6.

52. A(1,2); B(6,1); C(4,4); D(5,6);
E(2,3); F(2,5); G(3,2); H(0,4);
J(5,0); K(5½,3); L(1,½).

53.

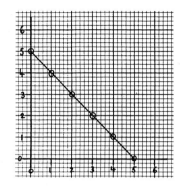

54.

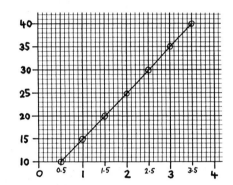

55. (a)(i)10 grams (ii)1 gram
(b)(i)£100 (ii)£10
(c)(i)4 litres (ii)0.4 litres
(d)(i)0.5mg (ii)0.05mg
(e)(i)20 minutes (ii)2 minutes
(f)(i)1000km (ii)100km
(g)(i) $20 (ii) $2
(h)(i)1 tonne (ii)0.1 tonne
(i)(i)1250 units (ii)125 units
(j)(i)5% (ii)0.5%

56.

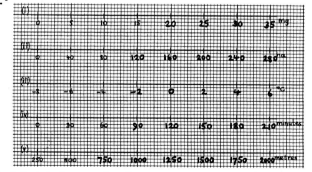

(b)(i)(i)5mg (ii)0.5mg
(ii)(i)40ha (ii)4ha
(iii)(i)2°C (ii)0.2°C
(iv)(i)30 minutes (ii)3 minutes
(v)(i)250 metres (ii)25 metres

57. (a)1cm (b)5p (c)12p (d)18p (e)1988
(f)1983 (g)1989 (h)1985 and 1987

58.

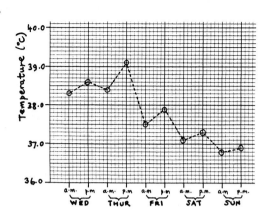

59.

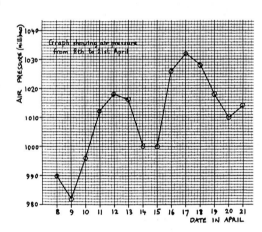

60. (a),(c),(d)

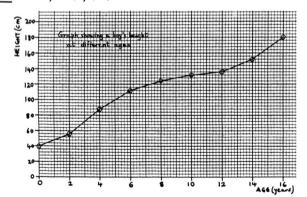

(b)4cm (e)2 and 4 (f)10 and 12
(g)(i)72cm (ii)144cm

61.

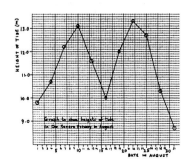

(a)12.8m (b)9.8m (c)4th or 5th, 14th,
17th or 18th, 27th

62.

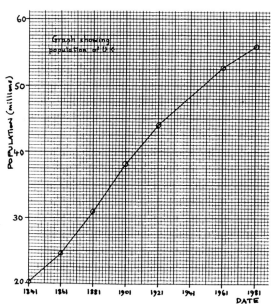

(b) 1881 to 1901
(c) (i) 34.5 million (ii) 41 million
    (iii) 48.5 million   (iv) between
    about 57 million and 59 million.
(d) Because World War II was in
    progress.

63. (a) about £146
    (b) about £236
    (c) about 7.3 years
    (d) about 11.6 years
    (e) about £400
    (f) £145
    (g) £265
    (h) about 6.7 years
    (i) about 13.3 years
    (j) Nicola, about £15 more
    (k) Lucy, about £35 more

64.

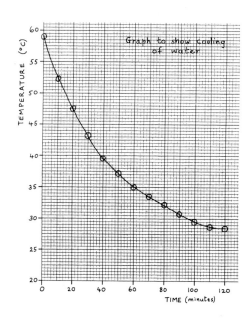

65. (a) Mass 300g, stretch 2.4cm
             400g,   3.4cm
             500g,   5.0cm
             600g,   6.7cm
             700g,   8.6cm
             800g,   10.8cm
             900g,   12.9cm
    (b),(c)

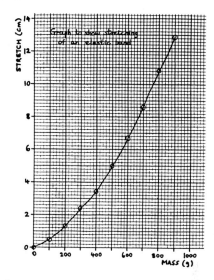

    (d) (i) about 4cm   (ii) about 10cm
        (iii) between about 15cm and 16cm

66.

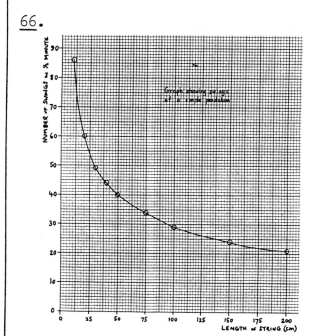

67. (a) (i) 270 litres (ii) 400 litres
            (iii) 50 litres
    (b) (i) 90 litres   (ii) 110 litres
        (iii) 40 litres
    (c) (i) 13th   (ii) 9th
    (d) 18th
    (e) 19th
    (f) 70 litres
    (g) 10th and 17th
    (h) Tuesday

68.(a)(i)about 260 Hz (ii)about 350 Hz
   (iii)about 145 Hz (iv)660 Hz
   (v)about 195 Hz.
 (b)(i)E above middle C (ii)C below
   middle C (iii)D above the C above
   middle C (iv)F below middle C
   (v)B above middle C.
 (c)(i)110 Hz, 220 Hz, 440 Hz
   (ii)The next higher A is twice the
     frequency (×2); the next lower A
     is half the frequency (÷2)
   (iii)55 Hz
   (iv)880 Hz
 (d)370 Hz
 (e)(i)D sharp(D#)above the C above
       middle C
   (ii)G sharp(G#) below middle C
   (iii)A sharp(A#) above middle C.

69.(a),(b).Suggested scales: volume
     axis 1cm for 25cm³, mass axis 1cm
     for 100g.

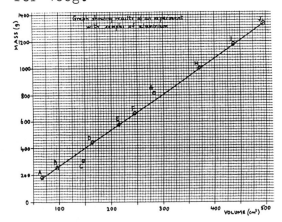

 (c)(i)about 335cm (ii)about 520cm
 (d)2.7
 (e)C and G

70.Suggested scales: temperature axis
   1cm for 10°C, solubility axis 1cm for
   5g.

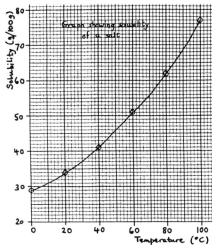

 (a)about 46g/100g (b)about 57g/100g

71.(a)0.1 horse power (b)100 watts
   (c)3000 watts (d)1200 watts (e)3.1
   horse power (f)4.7 horse power

72.(a)0.1 ounce (b)2 grams (c)82
   (d)136 (e)5.7 (f)2.4
 (g)142g flour, 28g cocoa, 56g(or 57g)
   sugar, 113g (or 114g) butter, half
   an egg.

73.

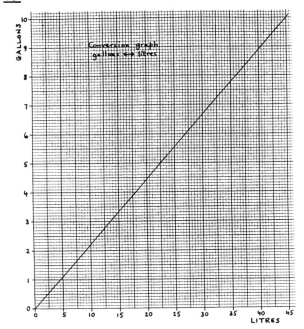

 (a)6.7 gallons (b)3.8 gallons
 (c)9.0 gallons (d)34.5 litres
 (e)10.5 litres.

74.

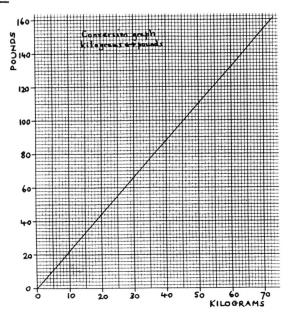

 (a)2 lb (b)35 lb (c)145 lb (d)52 kg
 (e)36 kg (f)45.5 kg (g)59.5 lb
 (h)(i)59000 kg (ii) 59 t

<u>75.</u>

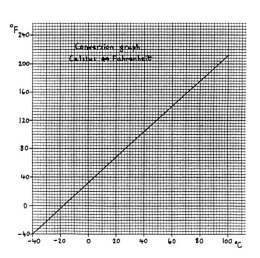

(a) 32°F
(b) 158°F
(c) 82°F
(d) 82°C
(e) 42°C

<u>76.</u>(a) 14.8 acres
   (b) 6.4 acres
   (c) 11.6 acres
   (d) 3.6 ha
   (e) 7.7 ha

<u>77.</u>(a)

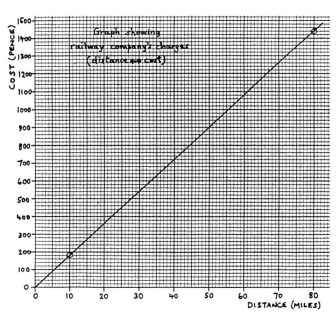

(b)(i)£11.20   (ii)£6.70
   (iii)£3.60   (iv)£13.10

(c)(i)41 miles   (ii)28 miles
   (iii)53 miles

<u>78.</u>

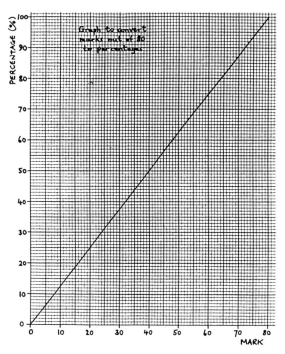

(a)56%   (b)70%   (c)62   (d)Yes. He
scores over 86%   (e)No. She scores
over 46%.

<u>79.</u>

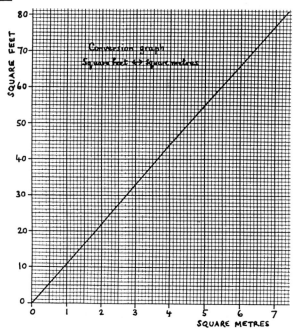

(a)33 square feet (b)60.5 square feet
(c)6.7m²   (d)4.3m²   (e)2.1m²
(f)(i)6.25m²   (ii)69 square feet
(g)The picture with area 3.6m²

<u>80.</u>(a)£45   (b)£108   (c)265
   (d)135

81.

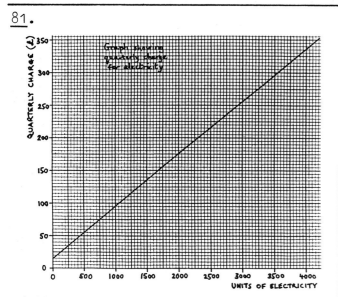

(a)about £215 (b)about £110
(c)about £305 (d)about 1690 units

82.

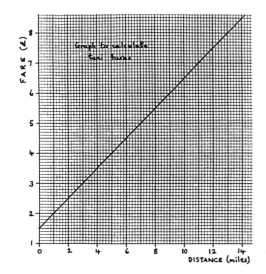

(a)£4.00 (b)£8.50 (c)£4.80
(d)9 miles (e)4 miles

83. Suggested scales: £ axis 1 cm for
£1, grunts axis 1 cm for 5 Gr.

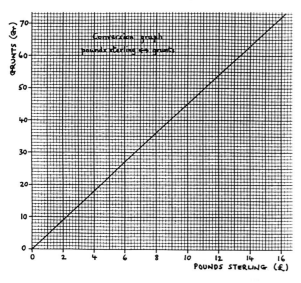

(a)£13.00 (b)40.5Gr (c)£6.40
(d)510Gr (e)£156 (f)Slurpia
(g)7p (h)50sz

84. (a)15 (b)6 a.m. (c)8 p.m.
(d)3 p.m. (e)8 a.m. (f)1 p.m.
(g)165°W (h)150°E (i)105°W
(j)75°E (k)98°E
(l)(i)11 p.m. (ii) 8 p.m.
(m)Because it is about 4 a.m. in Los
Angeles and the friend is probably
asleep.

85. (a),(b),(c) Suggested scales:
distance axis 1cm for 50km, petrol
axis 1cm for 5 litres.

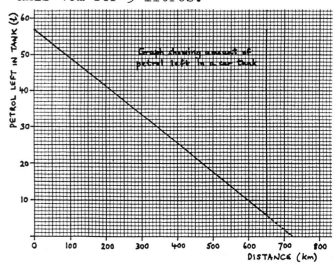

(d)(i)37.5 litres (ii)420km
(e)about 720km

86. Suggested scales: units axis 1cm
for 100 units, charges axis 1cm for
£5.

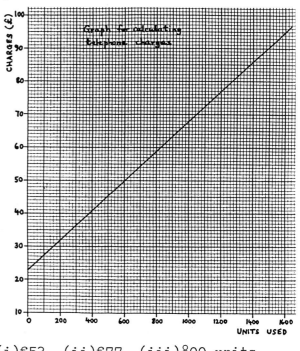

(i)£52 (ii)£77 (iii)800 units

87.

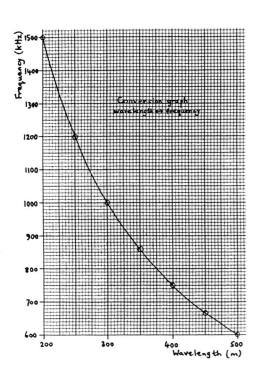

(c)1400kHz   (d)315m

88.(a)Victoria set off from the farmhouse and walked to the <u>hilltop</u>.

(b)She set off at 1102 a.m. and arrived at <u>1106</u> a.m.

(c)Rebecca set off running from the haunted barn at <u>1107</u> a.m. and reached the hilltop at <u>1108</u> a.m.

(d)She rested on the hilltop for <u>3</u> minutes.

(e)She reached the <u>farmhouse</u> at 1112 a.m.

(f)Helen set off from the <u>farmhouse</u> at <u>1109</u> a.m. (or the hilltop just after 1113 a.m.) and ran to the haunted barn, arriving there at <u>1115</u> a.m.

(g)The hilltop is <u>350</u>m from the farmhouse.

(h)The hilltop is <u>200</u>m from the haunted barn.

(i)The haunted barn is <u>550</u>m from the farmhouse.

(j)Helen passed Rebecca <u>150</u>m from the hilltop.

(k)Rebecca reached the hilltop <u>2</u> minutes after Victoria.

(l)She would have met Rebecca about <u>80</u>m from the haunted barn.

89.(a),(c),(e),(f)

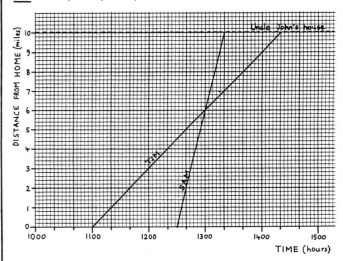

(b)20 minutes   (d)3 miles   (g)1420
(h)12 miles/h   (j)(i)1300
(ii)6 miles   (iii)4 miles

90.(a),(b),(c)

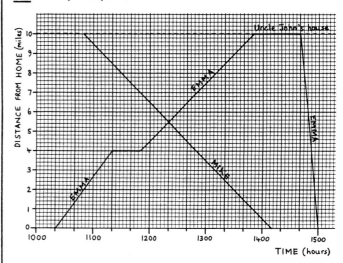

(d)3 miles/h   (e)50 minutes
(f)30miles/h   (g)1410
(h)(i)1220   (ii)5.5 miles

91. (a)$\frac{1}{2}$ minute   (b)100m   (c)300m
(d)300m/min   (e)$1\frac{1}{2}$ minutes
(f)2200m   (g)200m/min   (h)12000
(i)12km/h   (j)$12\frac{1}{2}$ min

92.(a)1508   (b)1539   (c)1532
(d)about 1615   (e)(i)6 miles
(ii)36 miles   (iii)36 miles/h
(f)48 miles/h   (g)12 minutes
(h)25 miles   (i)just before 1540
(j)about 19 miles

93.(a),(b),(c)

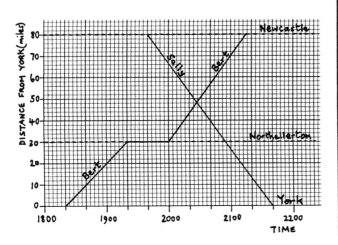

(d)about 2116

(e)40 miles/h

(f)(i)about 48 miles
(ii)about 32 miles
(iii)about 2028

94.(a),(b),(c),(d)

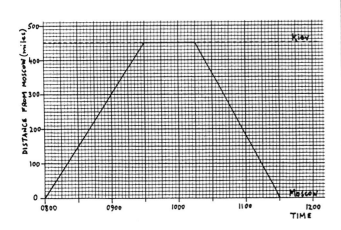

(e)300 miles

(f)300 miles/h

(g)360 miles

(h)360 miles/h

(i)327 miles/h (Total distance 900
miles, total time 2¾ hours)

95.(a),(b),(c),(d)

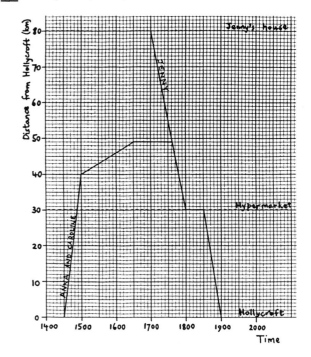

(e)(i)49km   (ii)about 1736
(iii)60km/h

96.(a),(c),(d)

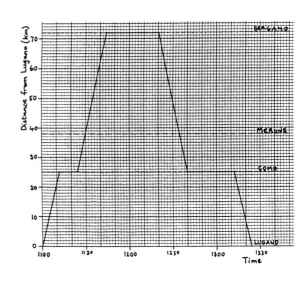

(b)2 minutes   (e)about 1130 and 1234

97.(a)4   (b)2   (c)10.5s   (d)14s
(e)about 71 metres   (f)about 7.1m/s
(g)about 24 metres   (h)7s
(i)He probably stops
(j)Because the sound of the gun takes
about ⅓ second to reach the finish
line. Timing from the sound of the
gun would make everybody (except
perhaps Harry) seem faster than he
or she really was.

98.(a),(b)

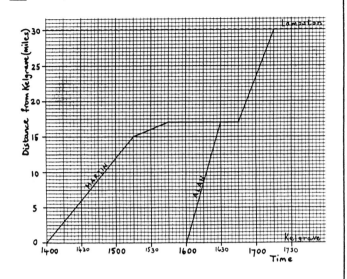

(c)12 miles/h
(d)1545
(e)45 minutes
(f)34 miles/h
(g)13 miles
(h)26 miles/h

99.

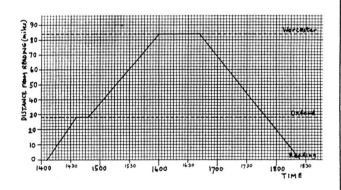

(a)(i)56 miles/h   (ii)about 47 miles/h
   (iii)about 49 miles/h

100.(a)9.35 a.m.
   (b)$\frac{1}{2}$ mile
   (c)10 minutes
   (d)$5\frac{1}{4}$ miles
   (e)50 minutes
   (f)11.05 a.m.
   (g)$5\frac{3}{4}$ miles
   (h)10 minutes
   (i)$15\frac{3}{4}$ miles/h
   (j)$34\frac{1}{2}$ miles/h

101.(a),(b),(c)

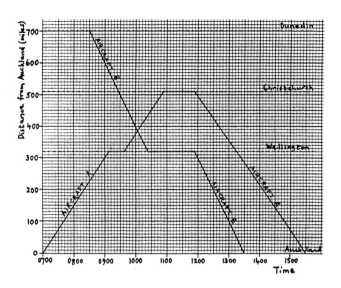

(d)(i)1054
   (ii)1154
   (iii)about 1315
   (iv)about 140 miles/h
   (v)380 miles
   (vi)1330
   (vii)about 1003
   (viii)about 65 miles

102.(a),(b),(c),(d)

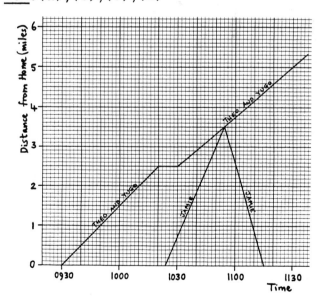

(e)(i)1020
   (ii)1054
   (iii)$3\frac{1}{2}$ miles
   (iv)10 miles/h

103.(a)6 miles/h
(b)2 miles/h
(c)7 miles/h
(d)20 miles/h
(e)30 miles/h
(f)10m/s
(g)20km/h
(h)8 miles/h
(i)0 m/s
(j)5m/s
(k)$2\frac{1}{2}$km/h
(l)15m/s
(m)25 miles/h
(n)125km/h
(o)$12\frac{1}{2}$m/s
(p)$4\frac{1}{2}$ miles/minute

104.(a)$1\frac{1}{2}$ min
(b)0.2 mile

(c) Train A

Kingston	d	0612
Richmond	d	0630
Barnes	d	0636
Clapham Jnc	d	0645
Waterloo	a	0654

Train B

Waterloo	d	0615
Clapham Jnc	d	0624
Barnes	d	0630
Richmond	d	0639
Kingston	a	0654

Train C

Waterloo	d	0645
Clapham Jnc	d	0654
Barnes	d	0700
Richmond	d	0709
Kingston	a	0724

(d)9.8 miles
(e)11.2 miles
(f)(i)0634 (ii)1.1 miles
(g)(i)0650 (ii)2 miles
(h)30 minutes
(i)9 minutes

105.

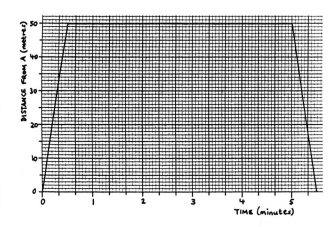

(a)$1\frac{2}{3}$m/s
(b)Exactly the same as Daniel's.
(c)(i)314m (ii)3.5m/s

1.(a)Jackmans
  (b)High Burnsby House
  (c)The Tower
  (d)Viney Cottage
  (e)Roundabout
  (f)Garage
  (g)Lindley Wood
  (h)Long Consett Farm
  (i)Grayland
  (j)Kingfield House

2.The Meadow (2,1)
  Gooding Beck House (9,8)
  Burnsby Grange (1,7)
  Napier Hill (10,4)
  Pond (4,5)
  Shackleton Arms Hotel (2,4)
  Old Mill (5,9)
  Pickstone Manor Farm (9,5)
  Bridge (1,11)
  Reeve Green (0,9)

3.(a)(7,6); (b)(5,5); (c)(7,8);
  (d)(6,6); (e)(5,10).

4.(a)Burnsby Grange
  (b)Burnsby Station
  (c)Roundabout
  (d)The Tower
  (e)The Tower and Pickstone Manor
      Farm

5.(Check that the coordinates are the
 correct way round, i.e. x (along)
 first, then y (up).)

6.(a),(b),(c),(d)

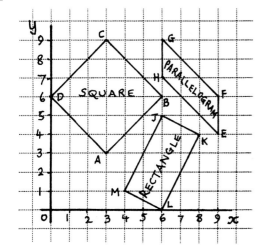

 (e)(i)6
    (ii)3
    (iii)4
    (iv)9
    (v)5

7.

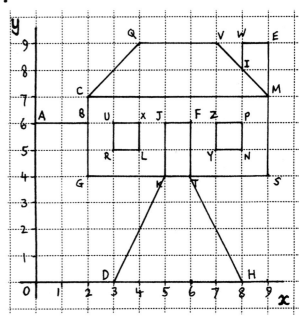

8.(a)Picnic Area
  (b)Katanga Canyon
  (c)Kiddies Kingdom
  (d)Pagoda Fountain
  (e)Land of Make Believe
  (f)Entrance
  (g)Conservatories
  (h)Festival Park
  (i)Mini Golf
  (j)Coach Park

9.Andrew (6,1)   Jamil (5,-5)
  Brenda (6,-3)   Karen (-3,-2)
  Carrie (-3,-5)   Lee (8,3)
  David (6,-8)   Mohammed (-6,4)
  Emma (-2,6)   Nelson (-4,-6)
  Frances (-5,-1)   Patrick (3,5)
  George (1,-6)   Ruth (-2,1)
  Helen (1,1)

10.Bowler (-3,0)
   Extra cover (-2,4)
   Fine leg (8,-1)
   Long on (-7,-5)
   Mid on (-3,-2)
   Mid wicket (0,-4)
   Silly mid off (-1,1)
   Slip (3,1)
   Square leg (2,-3)
   Third man (6,5)
   Wicket keeper (3,0)

11.

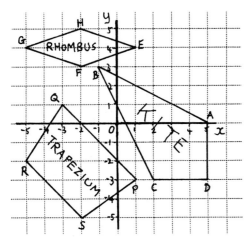

12.

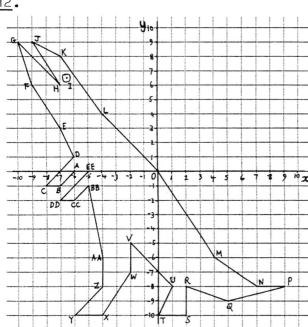

13.

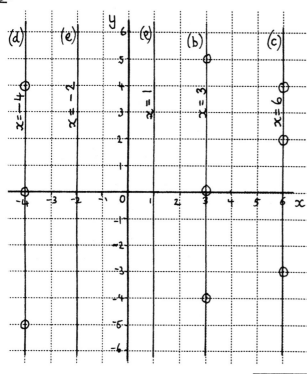

14. (a),(b),(c),(d),(f)

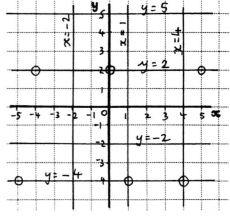

(e)(4,2)

15. (a) x=4   (f) Van Ness Avenue
(b) y=1   (g) Laguna Street
(c) x=-4   (h) Broadway
(d) y=-2   (i) Octavia Street
(e) y=0   (j) Bush Street

16. (a)(1,-4)
(b)(-4,2)
(c)(3,0)
(d)(4,4)
(e)(-5,-2)
(f) Laguna Street and Sacramento
    Street
(g) Octavia Street and Sutter Street
(h) Webster Street and Pacific Street
(i) Franklin Street and Sacramento
    Street
(j) Larkin Street and Vallejo Street

17. (a),(b)

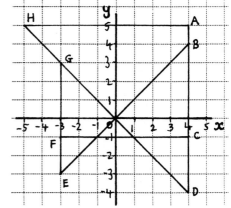

(c) EG is the graph of x=-3
    AH is the graph of y=5
    CF is the graph of y=-1
    BE is the graph of y=x
    DH is the graph of y=-x

18.(a),(b)

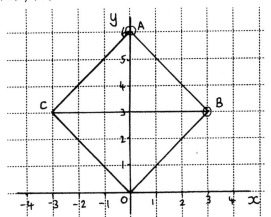

(c)OA is part of the graph of x=0
   OB is part of the graph of y=x
   CB is part of the graph of y=3
   OC is part of the graph of y=-x

(d)18 square units

19.

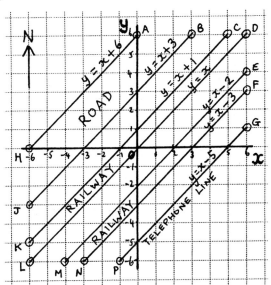

20.

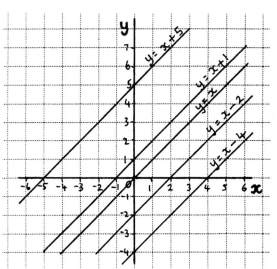

21.

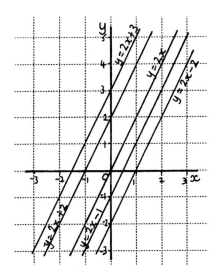

22.(a),(b)

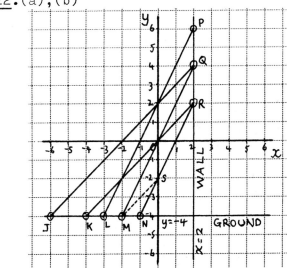

(c)The equation of PL is y=2x+2
   The equation of JQ is y=x+2
   The equation of KR is y=x
   The equation of MQ is y=2x
   The equation of NR is y=2x-2

(d)Parallelogram

23.(a),(b),(c),(d),(e)

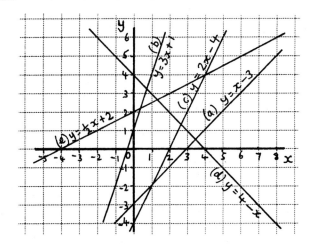

23.(continued) (f),(g),(h),(i),(j)

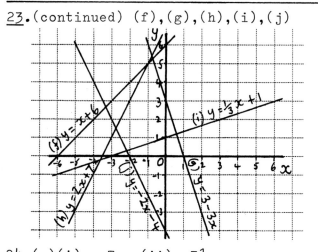

24.(a)(i)y=-7   (ii)x=3½
   (b)(i)y=3   (ii)x=1½
   (c)(i)y=6   (ii)x=-4
   (d)(i)y=-3   (ii)x=6
   (e)(i)y=5   (ii)x=-1
   (f)(i)y=6   (ii)x=6
   (g)(i)y=1½   (ii)x=-3
   (h)(i)y=-5   (ii)x=-1
   (i)(i)y=4½   (ii)x=-4½
   (j)(i)y=8   (ii)x=2

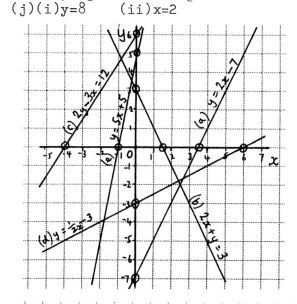

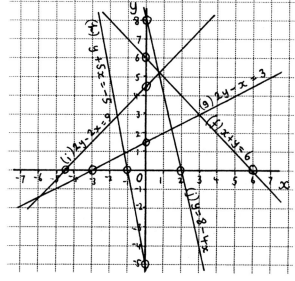

25.(a)3   (e)4   (i)$\frac{1}{6}$
   (b)7   (f)1½   (j)$\frac{3}{4}$
   (c)1   (g)$\frac{1}{2}$
   (d)$\frac{1}{5}$ (h)2

26.(a)(i)$\frac{1}{8}$ (ii)$\frac{1}{6}$ (iii)$\frac{1}{4}$
        (iv)$\frac{1}{2}$
   (b)$\frac{1}{5}$

27.(a)1   (e)1½   (i)7
   (b)3   (f)2   (j)$\frac{2}{3}$
   (c)4   (g)5
   (d)$\frac{1}{2}$ (h)$\frac{1}{4}$

28.(a)2   (e)$\frac{1}{4}$ (i)$\frac{1}{2}$
   (b)4   (f)6   (j)$\frac{3}{4}$
   (c)3   (g)$\frac{1}{3}$
   (d)1   (h)5

29.(i),(ii)

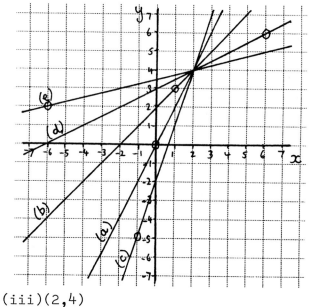

(iii)(2,4)

30.(a)4   (e)-1   (i)-$\frac{1}{2}$
   (b)-2   (f)-4   (j)-5
   (c)-3   (g)-2
   (d)1   (h)3

31.(a)-1   (c)-3   (e)-4
   (b)-$\frac{1}{3}$ (d)-2

<u>32</u>.(a),(b)

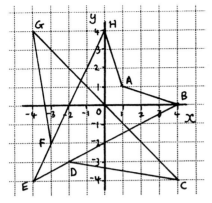

(c)EH 2; GC -1; AH -3; FG -6;

EB $\frac{1}{2}$; AB $-\frac{1}{3}$; DC $-\frac{1}{6}$

(d)(i)y=-x   (ii)y=2x+4
  (iii)y=$\frac{1}{2}$x-2

<u>33</u>.(a)(i)1 (ii)2 │ (f)(i)$\frac{1}{2}$ (ii)1
    (b)(i)2 (ii)-1 │ (g)(i)1 (ii)2$\frac{1}{2}$
    (c)(i)3 (ii)0 │ (h)(i)3 (ii)5
    (d)(i)-1 (ii)4 │ (i)(i)-2 (ii)3
    (e)(i)1 (ii)-4 │ (j)(i)4 (ii)-3

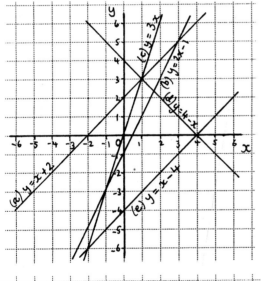

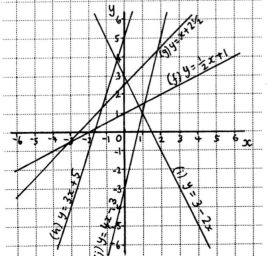

<u>34</u>.(a)(i)1   (ii)3   (iii)y=x+3
    (b)(i)-2   (ii)0   (iii)y=-2x
    (c)(i)3   (ii)-4   (iii)y=3x-4
    (d)(i)-1   (ii)2   (iii)y=2-x
                             (or y=-x+2)
    (e)(i)$\frac{1}{2}$ (ii)-3   (iii)y=$\frac{1}{2}$x-3

<u>35</u>.(a)y=2x-3
    (b)y=x+$\frac{1}{2}$
    (c)y=-3
    (d)y=3x
    (e)y=-x (or x+y=0)
    (f)y=x-2
    (g)x=-2
    (h)y=$-\frac{1}{2}$x+4 (or y=4$-\frac{1}{2}$x)
    (i)y=4x-5

    (j)y=$\frac{2}{3}$x (or y=$\frac{2x}{3}$)

<u>36</u>.

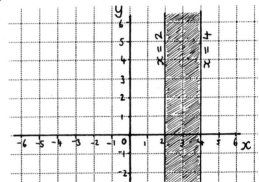

<u>37</u>.

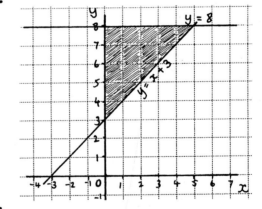

<u>38</u>.

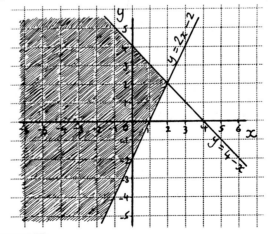

21

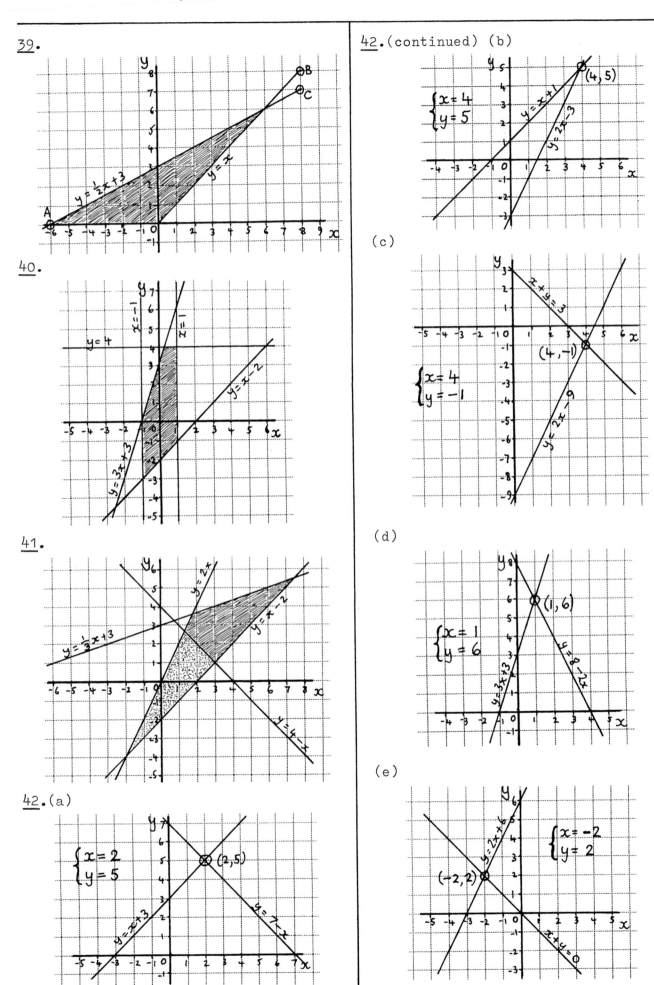

39.

40.

41.

42.(a)

42.(continued) (b)

(c)

(d)

(e)

22

42.(continued) (f)

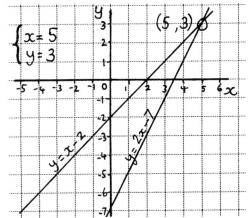

$\begin{cases} x = 5 \\ y = 3 \end{cases}$

(g)

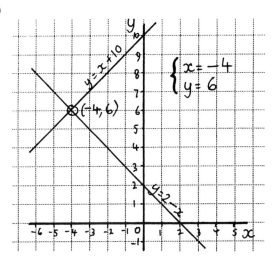

$\begin{cases} x = -4 \\ y = 6 \end{cases}$

(h)

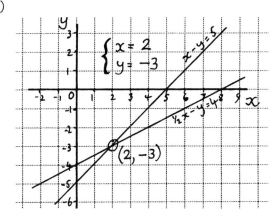

$\begin{cases} x = 2 \\ y = -3 \end{cases}$

(i)

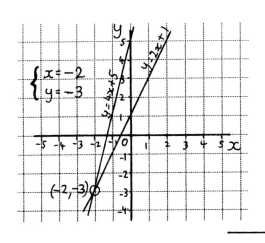

$\begin{cases} x = -2 \\ y = -3 \end{cases}$

42.(continued) (j)

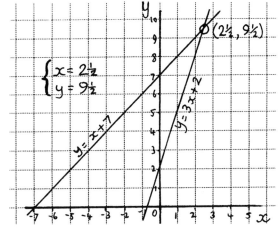

$\begin{cases} x = 2\frac{1}{2} \\ y = 9\frac{1}{2} \end{cases}$

43.(a)O (b)R (c)3 along, 4 up
(d)4 along, 3 up

44.(a)G (b)$\binom{3}{4}$ (c)$\binom{3}{1}$ (d)$\binom{4}{0}$
(e)$\binom{1}{4}$ (f)$\binom{0}{2}$ (g)To E, $\binom{4}{4}$

45.(a)$\binom{2}{2}$ (b)$\binom{1}{1}$ (c)$\binom{3}{3}$ (d)$\binom{4}{3}$ (e)$\binom{0}{4}$
(f)$\binom{1}{3}$ (g)$\binom{2}{0}$ (h)$\binom{0}{2}$ (i)$\binom{2}{-1}$ (j)$\binom{-1}{3}$

46. A$\binom{3}{3}$, B$\binom{0}{3}$, C$\binom{1}{-4}$, D$\binom{-4}{0}$,
E$\binom{5}{2}$, F$\binom{-3}{-2}$, G$\binom{4}{-5}$, U$\binom{2}{0}$, V$\binom{3}{-2}$,
W$\binom{-2}{-5}$.

47.(a),(b),(d)

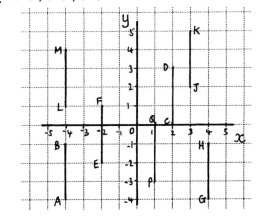

(c)(i) $\binom{5}{4}$ (ii) $\binom{-6}{1}$ (iii) $\binom{-6}{-4}$
(iv) $\binom{8}{-5}$ (v) $\binom{-1}{-2}$

23

<u>48</u>.(a),(b),(c),(d),(e)

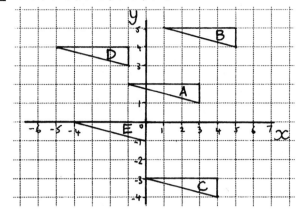

(f) E maps on to <u>B</u> by translating $\binom{5}{5}$

E maps on to D by translating $\binom{-1}{4}$

D maps on to C by translating $\binom{5}{-7}$

B maps on to <u>D</u> by translating $\binom{-6}{-1}$

<u>C</u> maps on to E by translating $\binom{-4}{3}$

<u>49</u>.(a),(b),(c),(d),(f)

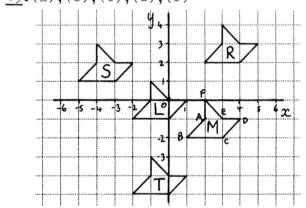

(e) $\binom{3}{3}$ (g) $\binom{0}{-4}$ (h) $\binom{-4}{-3}$ (i) $\binom{3}{-1}$

<u>50</u>.(a),(b),(c),(d)

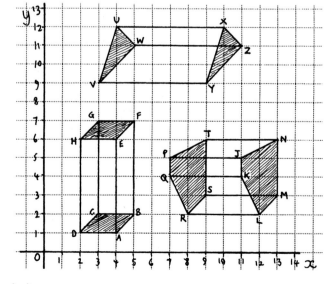

(e) prism

<u>51</u>.

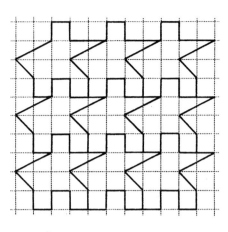

<u>52</u>.(Example)

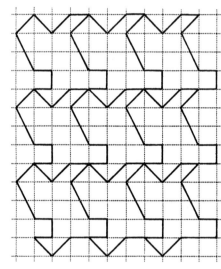

<u>53</u>.(i) M maps to **N** by translation $\binom{2}{3}$

(ii) M maps to P by translation $\binom{4}{-1}$

(iii) P maps to N by translation $\binom{-2}{4}$

(iv) N maps to Q by translation $\binom{-3}{-3}$

(v) Q maps to M by translation $\binom{1}{0}$

<u>54</u>.(i) C maps to D by translation $\binom{2}{2}$

(ii) C maps to E by translation $\binom{-5}{0}$

(iii) C maps to F by translation $\binom{5}{-1}$

(iv) C maps to G by translation $\binom{-3}{3}$

(v) C maps to H by translation $\binom{0}{-2}$

<u>55</u>.(Example)

<u>56.</u>

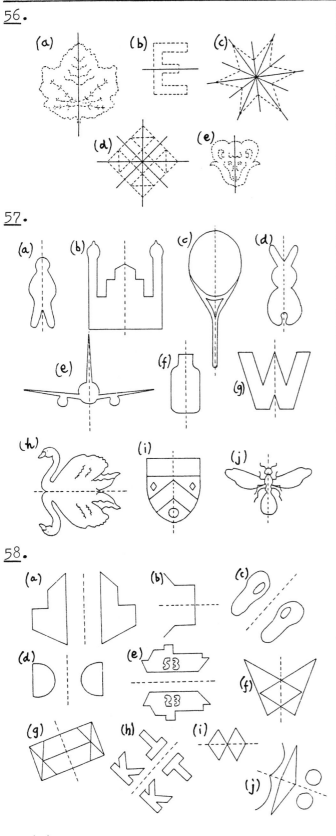

<u>57.</u>

<u>58.</u>

<u>59.</u>(a)B and F; C and E; H and Z;
J and P; K and V; L and Cancel;
M and S; O and W; Q and Y; T and
Number.
(Also flag position N is a reflection
of flag position U.)

(b)CAMP SURROUNDED. HELP

<u>60.</u>

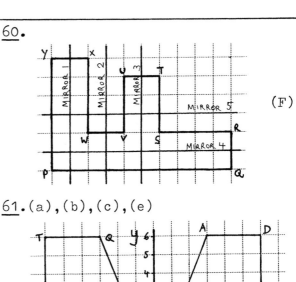

(F)

<u>61.</u>(a),(b),(c),(e)

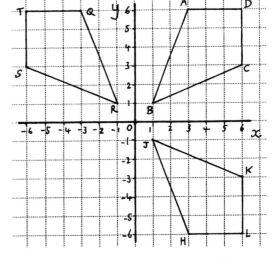

(d)H(3,-6)   (f)Q(-3,6)
   J(1,-1)   R(-1,1)
   K(6,-3)   S(-6,3)
   L(6,-6)   T(-6,6)

<u>62.</u>

<u>63.</u>(i)y axis <u>or</u> x=0
(ii)x=5
(iii)x axis <u>or</u> y=0
(iv)y=5
(v)y=-1
(vi)x=-1
(vii)y=3
(viii)x=1½

64.(a),(b),(d),(f)

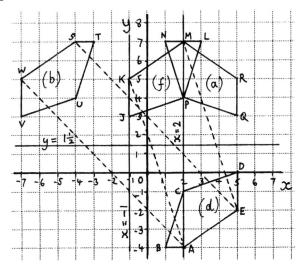

(c)Coordinates of V are (-7,3)
(e)Coordinates of E are (5,-2)
(g)Parallelograms

65.

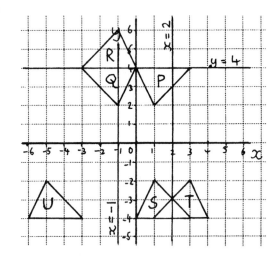

66.

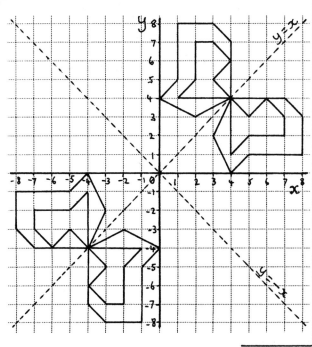

67.

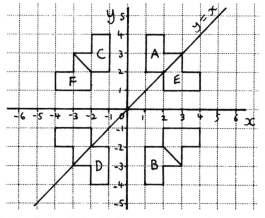

68.(a),(b),(c),(d)

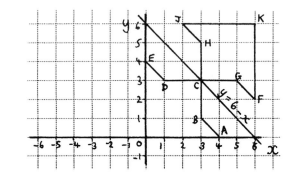

(e),(f)

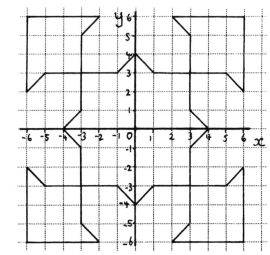

69.(a),(b),(c),(d),(e),(f)

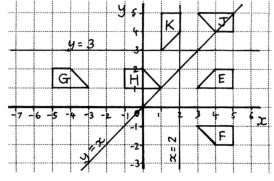

(g)Translation with shift vector $\begin{pmatrix} 0 \\ 6 \end{pmatrix}$

70.(b)

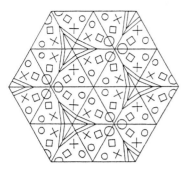

71.

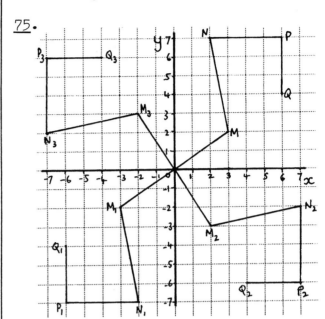

(vi) Reflection in y=2

(viii)Translation with shift

vector $\begin{pmatrix} 10 \\ -5 \end{pmatrix}$

72.(i)Translation with shift vector
$\begin{pmatrix} 3 \\ 5 \end{pmatrix}$
(ii)Reflection in x=3
(iii)Reflection in y axis (or
        reflection in x=0)
(iv)Translation with shift vector
$\begin{pmatrix} 6 \\ -4 \end{pmatrix}$
(v)Translation with shift vector $\begin{pmatrix} 8 \\ 0 \end{pmatrix}$
(vi)Reflection in y=2

73.A. Reflection in x=-4
D. Reflection in x=-1

E. Translation $\begin{pmatrix} 8 \\ 3 \end{pmatrix}$

H. Translation $\begin{pmatrix} 2 \\ -3 \end{pmatrix}$

I. Translation $\begin{pmatrix} 5 \\ -3 \end{pmatrix}$

L. Translation $\begin{pmatrix} 7 \\ -5 \end{pmatrix}$

P. Reflection in y=-1
S. Reflection in y=3

U. Translation $\begin{pmatrix} 3 \\ 3 \end{pmatrix}$

Y. Reflection in x=1

74.(a)4   (b)6   (c)4   (d)2
(e)5   (f)4   (g)2
(h)No rotational symmetry
(i)2   (j)3

75.

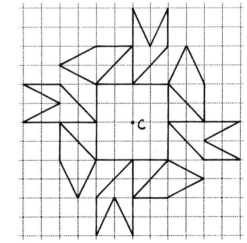

76.

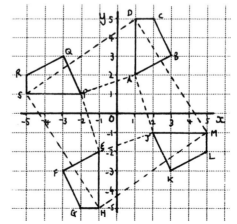

77.(a),(b),(d),(f)

(c)(-3,-3)
(e)(2,-1)
(g)Square

27

78.

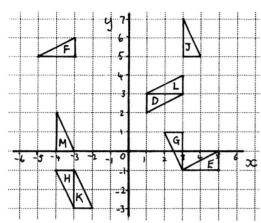

79.(a),(b),(c),(d)

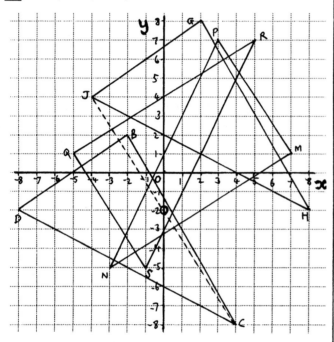

(e)Midpoint of CJ is (0,-2)

80.A to B: 180°, centre of rotation
(0,0)

A to C: 90° clockwise, centre of
rotation (0,0)

A to D: 90° anticlockwise, centre of
rotation (0,0)

A to E: 90° clockwise, centre of
rotation (2,3)

A to F: 180°, centre of rotation
(2,2)

A to G: 90° anticlockwise, centre of
rotation (2,5)

81.

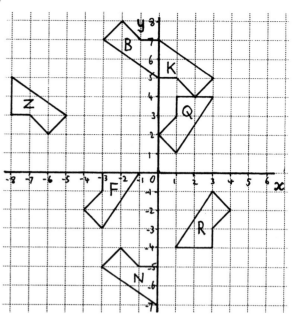

82.(a),(c)

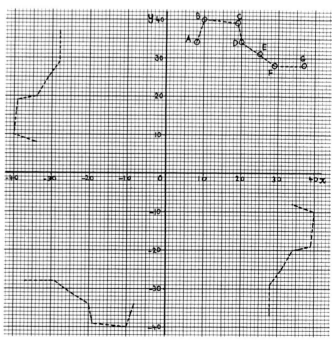

(b)Ursa Major (The Great Bear or
The Plough)

(d)Polaris (The Pole Star or α in
Ursa Minor)

83.

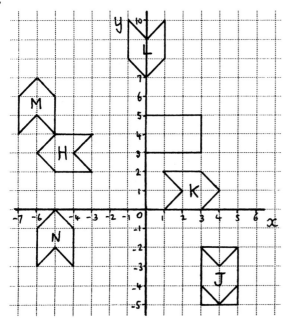

(j)(i)$(-1\frac{1}{2},3\frac{1}{2})$
(ii)$(2,2\frac{1}{2})$
(iii)$(3,7)$ or $(-1\frac{1}{2},5\frac{1}{2})$
(iv)$(-1\frac{1}{2},8\frac{1}{2})$ or $(-3,1)$
(v)$(-4\frac{1}{2},4\frac{1}{2})$ or $(1,-2)$

84.

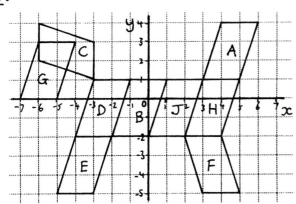

85.

A to B: Rotation 180° about O

A to C: Translation $\binom{3}{2}$

A to D: Reflection in the y axis

A to E: Rotation 90° anticlockwise about O

A to F: Translation $\binom{2}{-4}$

A to G: Rotation 180° about (-2,4)

A to H: Reflection in y=-1

A to J: Translation $\binom{-3}{-7}$

A to K: Rotation 180° about (-2,2)

A to L: Reflection in x=-3$\frac{1}{2}$

86.

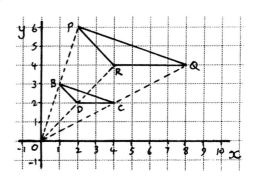

87.(a),(b)

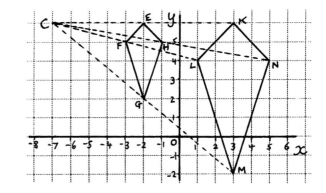

(c)EH and KN
GH and MN
FG and LM

88.

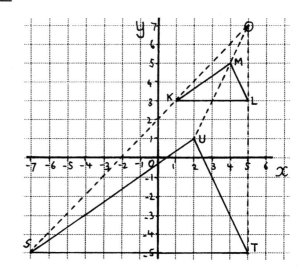

(c)(-7,-5)

(d)4

(e)$4 \times 3^2 = 36$

29

89.

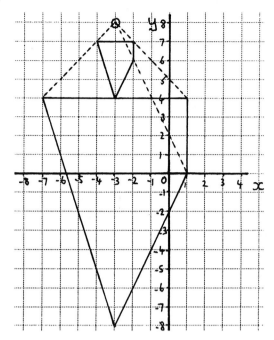

(c) $3\frac{1}{2} \times 4^2 = 56$

90.

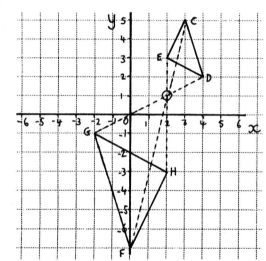

91.

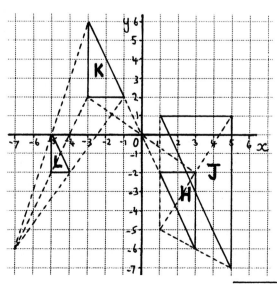

92.(a),(b),(c)

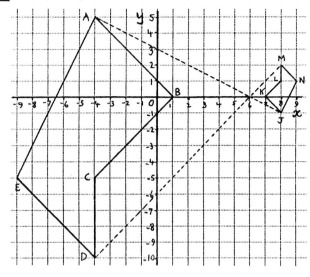

(d) $-\frac{1}{5}$

93.(a),(b)

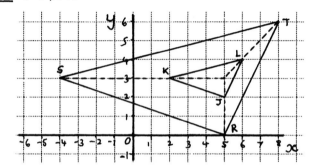

(c) R(5,0)
   S(-4,3)
   T(8,6)

94.(a)P to Q: centre (1,2),
          scale factor 2

(b)S to T: centre (-6,7),
          scale factor 3

(c)P to R: centre (0,0),
          scale factor -1

(d)S to M: centre (-5,4),
          scale factor 2

(e)R to N: centre (-3,-1),
          scale factor 2

95.(a),(b),(c)

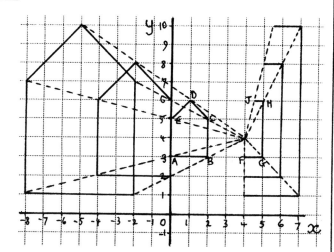

(d)

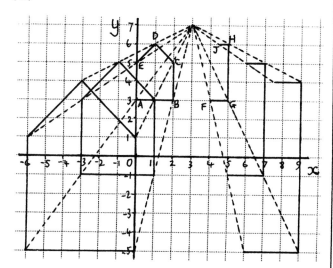

(e)(Example)

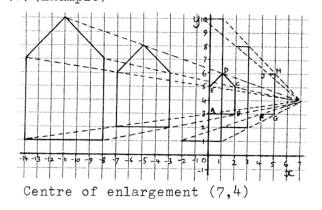

Centre of enlargement (7,4)

96.(a) $-\frac{1}{25}$

(b)6cm

(c)Upside down

(d)50cm

97.(a)35cm
(b)42cm
(c)30cm²
(d)1470cm²
(e)(i)4   (ii)480cm²
(f)(i)3   (ii)270cm²

98.

(a)

x	-4	-3	-2	-1	0	1	2	3	4
$4x$	-16	-12	-8	-4	0	4	8	12	16
+7	+7	+7	+7	+7	+7	+7	+7	+7	+7
y	-9	-5	-1	3	7	11	15	19	23

(b)

x	-4	-3	-2	-1	0	1	2	3	4
8	8	8	8	8	8	8	8	8	8
$-3x$	+12	+9	+6	+3	0	-3	-6	-9	-12
y	20	17	14	11	8	5	2	-1	-4

(c)

x	-4	-3	-2	-1	0	1	2	3	4
$2x$	-8	-6	-4	-2	0	2	4	6	8
-5	-5	-5	-5	-5	-5	-5	-5	-5	-5
y	-13	-11	-9	-7	-5	-3	-1	1	3

(d)

x	-4	-3	-2	-1	0	1	2	3	4
6	6	6	6	6	6	6	6	6	6
$-\frac{1}{2}x$	+2	$+1\frac{1}{2}$	+1	$+\frac{1}{2}$	0	$-\frac{1}{2}$	-1	$-1\frac{1}{2}$	-2
y	8	$7\frac{1}{2}$	7	$6\frac{1}{2}$	6	$5\frac{1}{2}$	5	$4\frac{1}{2}$	4

(e)

x	-4	-3	-2	-1	0	1	2	3	4
x^2	+16	+9	+4	+1	0	+1	+4	+9	+16
+4	+4	+4	+4	+4	+4	+4	+4	+4	+4
y	20	13	8	5	4	5	8	13	20

31

99.(a)

x	-4	-3	-2	-1	0	1	2	3	4
x^2	16	9	4	1	0	1	4	9	16
-8	-8	-8	-8	-8	-8	-8	-8	-8	-8
y	8	1	-4	-7	-8	-7	-4	1	8

(b)

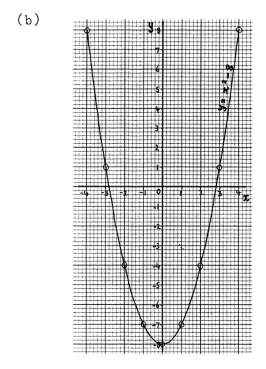

100.(a)

x	-3	-2	-1	0	1	2	3	4	5
x^2	9	4	1	0	1	4	9	16	25
-2x	+6	+4	+2	0	-2	-4	-6	-8	-10
-5	-5	-5	-5	-5	-5	-5	-5	-5	-5
y	10	3	-2	-5	-6	-5	-2	3	10

(b)

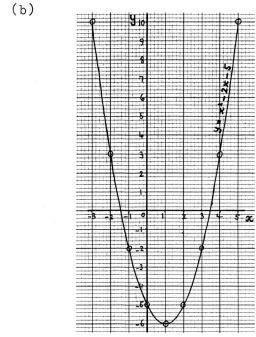

(c)Minimum value -6

101.(a)

x	-2	-1	0	1	2	3	4	5	6
4x	-8	-4	0	4	8	12	16	20	24
$-x^2$	-4	-1	0	-1	-4	-9	-16	-25	-36
+3	+3	+3	+3	+3	+3	+3	+3	+3	+3
y	-9	-2	3	6	7	6	3	-2	-9

(b),(c)

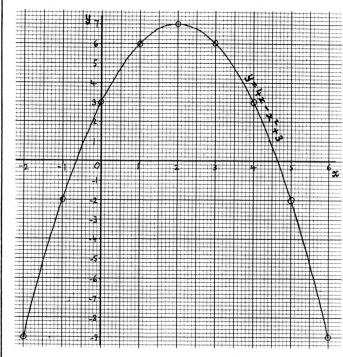

(d)Maximum value 7
(e)x=0.6, x=4.6 (approximate values)

102.(a)

x	-3	-2	-1	0	1	2	3
7	7	7	7	7	7	7	7
$-x^2$	-9	-4	-1	0	-1	-4	-9
y	-2	3	6	7	6	3	-2

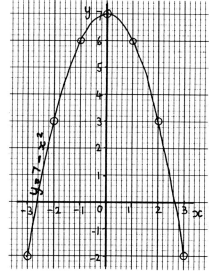

(b)x=2.6, x=-2.6 (approximate values)

103.(a)Between -6 and -7
     (Exact answer $-6\frac{1}{4}$)

 (b)$-\frac{1}{2}$

 (c)x=-3, x=2

 (d)A$(-4\frac{1}{2},9\frac{1}{2})$, B$(2\frac{1}{2},2\frac{1}{2})$

 (e)The striped area contains the set
    of points where y is greater than
    x^2+x-6 but less than 5-x.

104.(a),(b),(d),(f)

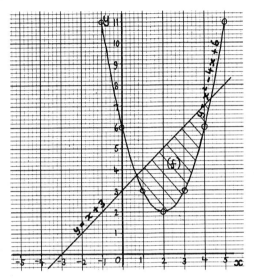

 (c)Minimum value 2
 (e)Approximately 0.7 and 4.3

105.(a)(i)x=-1.4, x=3.4

      (ii)x=-0.4, x=2.4

      (iii)x=-1.8, x=3.8

 (b)6

 (c)1

 (d)y=-75

106.(b)

x	-6	-5	-4	-3	-2	-1	0	1	2	3
x^2	36	25	16	9	4	1	0	1	4	9
+3x	-18	-15	-12	-9	-6	-3	0	3	6	9
-5	-5	-5	-5	-5	-5	-5	-5	-5	-5	-5
y	13	5	-1	-5	-7	-7	-5	-1	5	13

106.(continued)(a),(c)

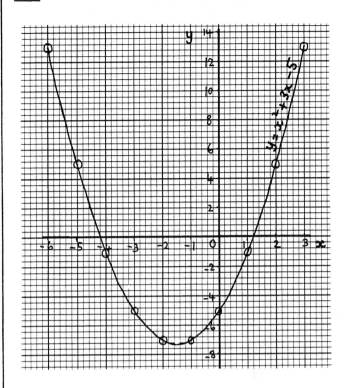

 (d)x=1.2, x=-4.2
 (e)$-1\frac{1}{2}$
 (f)$-7\frac{1}{4}$

107.(a),(b),(d)

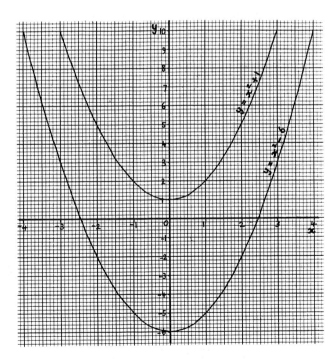

 (c)x=$2\frac{1}{2}$, x=$-2\frac{1}{2}$ (approximately)
 (e)Because it does not cross or
    touch the line y=0
 (f)Because the solution to $x^2+1=0$ is
    x=$\sqrt{-1}$ and a negative number
    cannot have a square root.

108.(a),(b),(c),(d),(e),(f),(h),(i),
(j),(k)

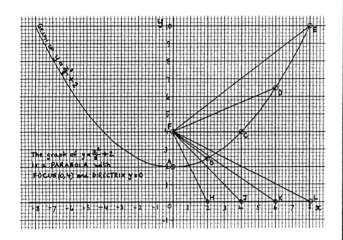

(g)Isosceles

110.(a),(b)

x	0	$\frac{1}{2}$	1	$1\frac{1}{2}$	2	3
x^2	0	0.25	1	2.25	4	9
$\sqrt{x}$	0	$\pm$0.7	$\pm$1	$\pm$1.22	$\pm$1.41	$\pm$1.73
y	0	0.35 or -0.35	1 or -1	1.84 or -1.84	2.84 or -2.84	5.20 or -5.20

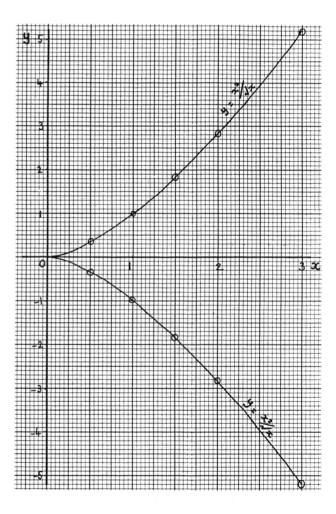

(c)Square roots of negative numbers have no real values.

109.(a),(b)

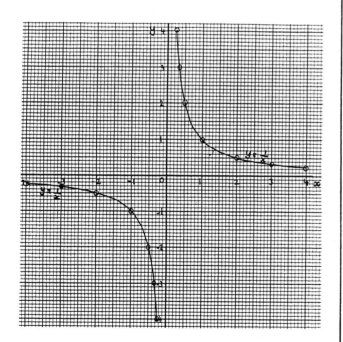

(c)The larger the value of x, the smaller the value of y, and vice versa, but neither value ever reaches zero.

111.(a),(d)

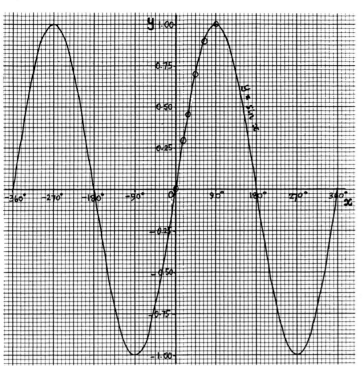

(b)(i)9°
   (ii)0.025

(c)sin 0° = 0
   sin 18° = 0.31
   sin 27° = 0.45
   sin 45° = 0.71
   sin 63° = 0.89
   sin 90° = 1

(e)sin −360° = 0
   sin −270° = 1
   sin −180° = 0
   sin −90° = −1
   sin 180° = 0
   sin 270° = −1
   sin 360° = 0

(f)(i)−0.59
   (ii)0.45
   (iii)−330°, −210°,
        30°, 150°

112.(a)

x	−3	−2	−1.4	−1	−0.5	0	0.5	1	1.4	2	3
x^3	−27	−8	−2.7	−1	−0.125	0	0.125	1	2.7	8	27
−6x	+18	+12	+8.4	+6	+3	0	−3	−6	−8.4	−12	−18
y	−9	4	5.7	5	2.875	0	−2.875	−5	−5.7	−4	9

(b)

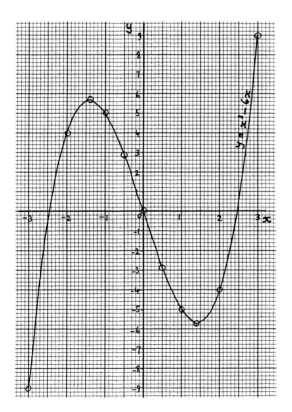

(c)(i)x=−2.4, x=0, x=2.4 (approximate values)
   (ii)x=−2.7, x=0.7, x=2 (approximate values)

35

113.(a)

x	-6	-5½	-5	-4	-2	0	2	4	5	5½	6
36	36	36	36	36	36	36	36	36	36	36	36
$-x^2$	-36	-30¼	-25	-16	-4	0	-4	-16	-25	-30¼	-36
y^2	0	5¾	11	20	32	36	32	20	11	5¾	0
y	0	2.4 or -2.4	3.3 or -3.3	4.5 or -4.5	5.7 or -5.7	6 or -6	5.7 or -5.7	4.5 or -4.5	3.3 or -3.3	2.4 or -2.4	0

(b)

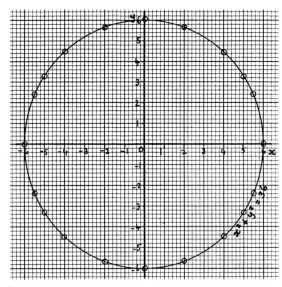

(c)Circle

114.B(5,2,0)   L(3,0,8)
    C(3,7,0)   M(5,0,6)
    D(6,5,0)   P(0,6,1)
    E(7,0,0)   Q(0,2,7)
    F(3,1,0)   R(0,7,3)
    H(8,0,7)   S(0,5,5)
    J(2,0,5)   T(0,8,6)
    K(1,0,1)

115.(i)A(6,3,5)
       B(9,1,3)
       C(4,1,4)
       D(10,3,7)
       E(3,2,6)
       F(8,4,2)
       G(7,4,1)
       H(9,0,6)

(ii)(12,5,8)

116.

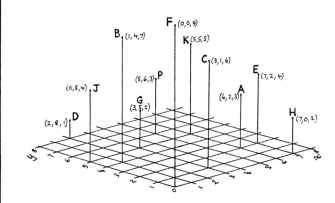

117.(a)(i)West
       (ii)South
       (iii)Down

   (b)(i)(3,3,0)
      (ii)(-3,1,0)
      (iii)(4,-3,3)
      (iv)(0,2,-1)
      (v)(-4,-3,-4)